Instant Cartoons
for Church Newsletters

George W. Knight *Compiler*

BAKER BOOK HOUSE
Grand Rapids, Michigan 49516

Copyright 1992 by Baker Book House Company

P.O. Box 6287
Grand Rapids, MI 49516-6287

ISBN: 0-8010-5255-6

Printed in the United States of America

The Laughs Go On

The church has a serious mission in the world, yet there is much to laugh about. You will find these glimpses of church life just as funny and wholesome as the cartoons in the previous books in this series. They are designed to add sparkle to your church bulletins and newsletters. Just clip and publish these cartoons to put a little spice and variety into your church publications.

Now that hundreds of these cartoons have been published in Baker's Instant Cartoons series, I am curious about which ones have drawn the most chuckles in your church. Write and let me know which cartoons have been most popular in your congregation. This will help me in selecting material for future books of Instant Cartoons. The address is Baker Book House, P. O. Box 6287, Grand Rapids, MI 49516.

George W. Knight

About the Cartoonists . . .

Doug Gray is a professional illustrator and cartoonist who lives in Fairfax, Virginia. His cartoons have appeared in a number of national publications, including *The Saturday Evening Post, Highlights for Children,* and *Personnel Journal.*

Charles Cartwright was a pioneer in the field of religious cartooning. He began creating church cartoons at the suggestion of his own pastor more than thirty years ago. His work appeared in such prestigious publications as *The Saturday Evening Post* and Bennet Cerf's *100 Best Cartoons of All Times.* Although he is deceased, his cartoons are still distributed by Al Smith Feature Service of Zephyrhills, Florida.

Joe McKeever is known as the "preaching cartoonist," since he is a pastor by vocation who enjoys poking fun at the humorous side of church life. He serves as pastor of the First Baptist Church of Kenner, Louisiana. His cartoons have been published in numerous Christian magazines as well as the previous six books in Baker's Instant Cartoons series.

"DAVID GOT INTO THE BIBLE WITH ONE OF THESE."

"THERE ISN'T ANYTHING IN THE TEN COMMANDMENTS ABOUT NOT CHEWING GUM."

"MY DAD SAYS THE LONGEST PRAYERS."

"DAVID GOT INTO THE BIBLE WITH ONE OF THESE."

"MY DAD SAYS THE LONGEST PRAYERS."

"THERE ISN'T ANYTHING IN THE TEN COMMANDMENTS
ABOUT NOT CHEWING GUM."

"HE HAS A FLARE FOR THEATRICS—
THEY NEVER HAVE TO PASS THE COLLECTION PLATE."

"IF GOD'S WITH ME, HOW COME HE DOESN'T
STRAIGHTEN THAT GUY'S CURVE BALL?"

"HALLELUJAH IS THE OLD-FASHIONED WAY
OF SAYING EXXX-CELLENT!"

"YA GOT A CHILD'S PLATE? . . . I ONLY GOT A NICKEL!"

"IF GOD'S WITH ME, HOW COME HE DOESN'T
STRAIGHTEN THAT GUY'S CURVE BALL?"

"HE HAS A FLARE FOR THEATRICS—
THEY NEVER HAVE TO PASS THE COLLECTION PLATE."

"YA GOT A CHILD'S PLATE?... I ONLY GOT A NICKEL!"

"HALLELUJAH IS THE OLD-FASHIONED WAY
OF SAYING EXXX-CELLENT!"

"HE WATCHED 'KING OF KINGS' ON THE LATE, LATE SHOW LAST NIGHT."

"NO, HE ISN'T A PANHANDLER."

"MY HARMONICA IS READY IF THE POWER GOES OUT AGAIN."

"NO, HE ISN'T A PANHANDLER."

"HE WATCHED 'KING OF KINGS' ON THE LATE, LATE SHOW LAST NIGHT."

"MY HARMONICA IS READY IF THE POWER GOES OUT AGAIN."

"YOU WOULD'VE ENJOYED TODAY'S SERMON, POPS . . . IT WAS ALL ABOUT THE TWELVE OLD FOSSILS."

"WE'LL HAVE AN ORDER OF LOAVES AND FISHES TO GO."

"REMEMBER, MOM, TO ERR IS HUMAN, TO FORGIVE IS DIVINE."

"I DIDN'T KNOW YOU PEOPLE BAPTIZED YOUR BUSES, TOO."

"WE'LL HAVE AN ORDER OF LOAVES AND FISHES TO GO."

"YOU WOULD'VE ENJOYED TODAY'S SERMON, POPS . . .
IT WAS ALL ABOUT THE TWELVE OLD FOSSILS."

"I DIDN'T KNOW YOU PEOPLE BAPTIZED
YOUR BUSES, TOO."

"REMEMBER, MOM, TO ERR IS HUMAN,
TO FORGIVE IS DIVINE."

"PLAY REVEILLE."

"IF YOU EVER NEED SERMON MATERIAL,
DR. CHADWICK, LET ME TELL YOU
ABOUT MY HUSBAND."

"I WARNED THEM THAT THE ORGAN WAS TOO BIG FOR THIS BUILDING."

"THEY REJECTED MY DEVIL'S FOOD CAKE."

"IF YOU EVER NEED SERMON MATERIAL, DR. CHADWICK, LET ME TELL YOU ABOUT MY HUSBAND."

"PLAY REVEILLE."

"THEY REJECTED MY DEVIL'S FOOD CAKE."

"I WARNED THEM THAT THE ORGAN WAS TOO BIG FOR THIS BUILDING."

"HE WRITES PRAYERS."

"I GUESS THEY'RE CHURCH MICE."

"USHER TRAINEES."

"LOOK, MOM! THE 'HOUSE OF THE LORD' HAS THE SAME FIX-IT MAN WE DO!"

"I GUESS THEY'RE CHURCH MICE."

"HE WRITES PRAYERS."

"LOOK, MOM! THE 'HOUSE OF THE LORD'
HAS THE SAME FIX-IT MAN WE DO!"

"USHER TRAINEES."

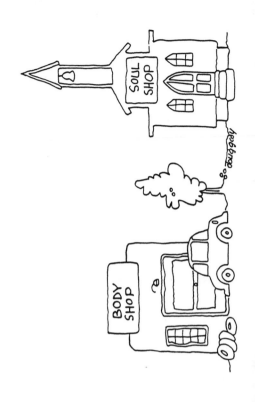

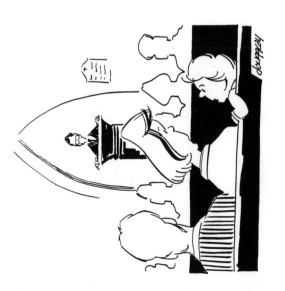

"CAN'T GOD GET HIS OWN NAME
SO WE DON'T HAVE TO PRAY TO HIM
IN JESUS' NAME ALL THE TIME?"

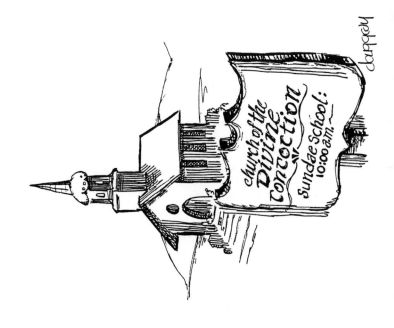

"IT HASN'T STOPPED RAINING SINCE WE HIRED THAT NEW WEATHERMAN!"

"CAN'T GOD GET HIS OWN NAME
SO WE DON'T HAVE TO PRAY TO HIM
IN JESUS' NAME ALL THE TIME?"

"IT HASN'T STOPPED RAINING SINCE WE
HIRED THAT NEW WEATHERMAN!"

"MOM, WE'RE IN CHURCH! ALL MY SQUIRMING
MUST BE GOD'S WILL."

"HIS DOCTOR RECOMMENDED GLASSES,
BUT HE OPTED FOR THE LARGE-PRINT EDITION."

"THE DEVIL TEMPTED EVE WITH AN APPLE, AND JUDGING BY THE EMPTY PEWS, HE TEMPTED ADAM WITH A GOLF BALL."

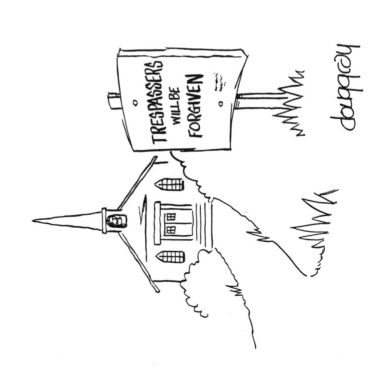

"HIS DOCTOR RECOMMENDED GLASSES, BUT HE OPTED FOR THE LARGE-PRINT EDITION."

"MOM, WE'RE IN CHURCH! ALL MY SQUIRMING MUST BE GOD'S WILL."

"THE DEVIL TEMPTED EVE WITH AN APPLE, AND JUDGING BY THE EMPTY PEWS, HE TEMPTED ADAM WITH A GOLF BALL."

"I URGE YOU TO GIVE GENEROUSLY
SO WE CAN MAKE BADLY NEEDED REPAIRS
TO THIS CHURCH."

"WE'D BE PLEASED TO HAVE YOU ENDOW A PEW,
MRS. SCOWCROFT, BUT WE SIMPLY COULDN'T
GUARANTEE THAT DEMOCRATS WOULD NEVER SIT IN IT."

"I INTENDED MAKING A SPECIAL APPEAL TO THE SACRIFICIAL GIVERS IN OUR CONGREGATION, BUT SINCE NEITHER IS HERE TODAY . . ."

"SINCE YOU'RE NEW HERE, YOUNG MAN, I'LL SHOW YOU WHICH MEMBERS TO CULTIVATE AND WHICH MEMBERS TO AVOID!"

"WE'D BE PLEASED TO HAVE YOU ENDOW A PEW, MRS. SCOWCROFT, BUT WE SIMPLY COULDN'T GUARANTEE THAT DEMOCRATS WOULD NEVER SIT IN IT."

"I URGE YOU TO GIVE GENEROUSLY SO WE CAN MAKE BADLY NEEDED REPAIRS TO THIS CHURCH."

"SINCE YOU'RE NEW HERE, YOUNG MAN, I'LL SHOW YOU WHICH MEMBERS TO CULTIVATE AND WHICH MEMBERS TO AVOID!"

"I INTENDED MAKING A SPECIAL APPEAL TO THE SACRIFICIAL GIVERS IN OUR CONGREGATION, BUT SINCE NEITHER IS HERE TODAY . . ."

"AND MAY THY WINTER FAITHFUL
NOT BECOME SUMMER DROPOUTS!"

YOU'VE GOT TO ADMIT THEY ECONOMIZE.
THEY MADE ONLY ONE COPY OF THE BUDGET,
IN CRAYOLA ON WRAPPING PAPER!"

"THIS IS THE FIFTH STRAIGHT NEW YEAR HE'S RESOLVED TO ATTEND CHURCH EVERY SUNDAY AND THE FIFTH STRAIGHT YEAR I'VE RESOLVED NOT TO GET MY HOPES UP!"

"I'M GLAD TO WELCOME BACK SOME OLD FAMILIAR FACES, NOW THAT THE PRO FOOTBALL SEASON HAS ENDED!"

"YOU'VE GOT TO ADMIT THEY ECONOMIZE.
THEY MADE ONLY ONE COPY OF THE BUDGET,
IN CRAYOLA ON WRAPPING PAPER!"

"AND MAY THY WINTER FAITHFUL
NOT BECOME SUMMER DROPOUTS!"

"I'M GLAD TO WELCOME BACK SOME OLD
FAMILIAR FACES, NOW THAT THE PRO FOOTBALL
SEASON HAS ENDED!"

"THIS IS THE FIFTH STRAIGHT NEW YEAR HE'S
RESOLVED TO ATTEND CHURCH EVERY SUNDAY
AND THE FIFTH STRAIGHT YEAR I'VE RESOLVED
NOT TO GET MY HOPES UP!"

"WE RENT A FEW DURING SUMMER MONTHS TO HELP ATTENDANCE LOOK BETTER."

"ALL THESE WEDDING REHEARSALS WITH JIMMY FINALLY DID THE TRICK! EDDIE HAS PROPOSED!"

"JUST GETTING HIMSELF TOUGHENED UP FOR THE CHURCH'S ANNUAL STEWARDSHIP DRIVE!"

© CHAS. CARTWRIGHT

"HERE'S OUR BANK STATEMENT— WELL, NOT EXACTLY A STATEMENT, MORE LIKE A QUESTION."

© CHAS. CARTWRIGHT

"ALL THESE WEDDING REHEARSALS WITH JIMMY FINALLY DID THE TRICK! EDDIE HAS PROPOSED!"

"WE RENT A FEW DURING SUMMER MONTHS TO HELP ATTENDANCE LOOK BETTER."

"HERE'S OUR BANK STATEMENT— WELL, NOT EXACTLY A STATEMENT, MORE LIKE A QUESTION."

"JUST GETTING HIMSELF TOUGHENED UP FOR THE CHURCH'S ANNUAL STEWARDSHIP DRIVE!"

"YOU'RE IMPROVING—THIS SUNDAY YOU MADE IT IN TIME FOR THE FINAL PRAYER!"

"PLEASE, HARRY, NEVER MIND THE DIME!"

"YOU HAVE A CHOICE OF THREE MEATS— MEAT LOAF WITH TOMATOES, MEAT LOAF WITH MUSHROOMS, OR MEAT LOAF PLAIN!"

"GROVER RESERVES EVERY SUNDAY TO SET AT LEAST ONE CHRISTIAN EXAMPLE FOR THE CHILDREN!"

"PLEASE, HARRY, NEVER MIND THE DIME!"

"YOU'RE IMPROVING—THIS SUNDAY YOU MADE IT
IN TIME FOR THE FINAL PRAYER!"

"GROVER RESERVES EVERY SUNDAY
TO SET AT LEAST ONE CHRISTIAN EXAMPLE
FOR THE CHILDREN!"

"YOU HAVE A CHOICE OF THREE MEATS—
MEAT LOAF WITH TOMATOES, MEAT LOAF
WITH MUSHROOMS, OR MEAT LOAF PLAIN!"

"I'VE RECENTLY RECEIVED SOME THREATENING LETTERS—LET ME READ YOU THIS ONE FROM THE MORTGAGE COMPANY."

"WE ALWAYS PUT ASIDE 10 PERCENT OF EVERYTHING FOR THE LORD. IT SHOULD BE A TIDY SUM BY THE TIME THE CHURCH INHERITS IT!"

"WISH THE TEACHER HADN'T TOLD US
THE FUTURE OF THE WORLD IS RESTING
ON OUR YOUNG CHRISTIAN SHOULDERS.
I WAS PLANNING TO BUILD A MODEL AIRPLANE
THIS WEEK."

"JUST A LITTLE TIP, YOUNG MAN.
IF YOU WANT TO BE POPULAR HERE,
STAY AWAY FROM CONTROVERSIAL ISSUES
SUCH AS SIN."

"WE ALWAYS PUT ASIDE 10 PERCENT OF EVERYTHING FOR THE LORD. IT SHOULD BE A TIDY SUM BY THE TIME THE CHURCH INHERITS IT!"

"I'VE RECENTLY RECEIVED SOME THREATENING LETTERS—LET ME READ YOU THIS ONE FROM THE MORTGAGE COMPANY."

"JUST A LITTLE TIP, YOUNG MAN. IF YOU WANT TO BE POPULAR HERE, STAY AWAY FROM CONTROVERSIAL ISSUES SUCH AS SIN."

"WISH THE TEACHER HADN'T TOLD US THE FUTURE OF THE WORLD IS RESTING ON OUR YOUNG CHRISTIAN SHOULDERS. I WAS PLANNING TO BUILD A MODEL AIRPLANE THIS WEEK."

"I THINK I'LL SUGGEST SERVING FREE COFFEE BEFORE THE SERVICE."

"DON'T YOU REMEMBER— I PUT IN A DOLLAR TWO SUNDAYS AGO!"

"EVEN WHEN HE'S ASLEEP HE FEELS HIS SOUL IS ABSORBING GOOD FROM THE SURROUNDING CHURCH ATMOSPHERE!"

"LUCKY THE FLOCK CAN'T SEE ITS SHEPHERD AT 7:30 A.M.!"

"DON'T YOU REMEMBER—
I PUT IN A DOLLAR TWO SUNDAYS AGO!"

"I THINK I'LL SUGGEST SERVING FREE COFFEE
BEFORE THE SERVICE."

"LUCKY THE FLOCK CAN'T SEE ITS SHEPHERD
AT 7:30 A.M.!"

"EVEN WHEN HE'S ASLEEP HE FEELS HIS SOUL
IS ABSORBING *GOOD* FROM THE SURROUNDING
CHURCH ATMOSPHERE!"

"FOR OUR MISSION TRIP THIS SUMMER, OUR KIDS ARE GOING TO THE BEACH AND MINISTER TO OTHER YOUTH CHOIRS!"

"OUR CHURCH HAS A HUNDRED THOUSAND DOLLARS WORTH OF PIANO AND ORGAN — AND THE WORSHIP MUSIC IS PROVIDED BY A TEN-DOLLAR TAPE!"

"ACTUALLY I WASN'T LOOKING FOR A FRIENDLY CHURCH SO MUCH AS FOR A FRIEND."

"PASTOR, REMEMBER HOW YOU DROPPED IN UNEXPECTEDLY TO INVITE ME TO CHURCH? WELL, IT'S MY TURN. LET'S GO INSIDE AND TALK INSURANCE!"

"WE'LL KNOW IF HE FINISHES BY NOON."

"GOOD EVENING, MYSTERY-LOVERS! IT'S TIME ONCE AGAIN FOR 'FUN' WITH THE COMMENTARIES!"

"MY LEG IS NOT INTERESTED IN THIS SERMON. IT HAS GONE TO SLEEP."

"DAD AND MOM ARE OUT RIGHT NOW — BUT I'LL BE GLAD TO MINISTER TO YOU!"

"YOUR JOB IS SAFE, PASTOR— —So preach it, Brother!"

"OH, PASTOR, THIS IS MR. SAMPSON. HE HAS RUN SEVERAL CORPORATIONS IN DALLAS AND IS MOVING TO OUR CITY. BEFORE JOINING US HE WANTS TO KNOW WHAT POWER VACANCIES OUR CHURCH HAS AT THE MOMENT."

"WE TOLD THE PASTOR SEARCH COMMITTEE WE WANTED SHORT SERMONS!"

WELCOME PASTOR MICHAEL SHORT

"JASON, DON'T EVER SAY ANYTHING YOU DON'T WANT THE WORLD TO HEAR!"

"THEIR LAST PASTOR O.D.'ED ON JOY."

FAITH CHURCH
"HAND-CLAPPING, GATORADE DOUSING, AMEN-SHOUTING FELLOWSHIP"

"DAD'S INSIDE LISTENING TO YOU PREACH ON TELEVISION—PERSONALLY, I DON'T THINK YOU OUGHT TO INTERRUPT YOURSELF!"

"THE VISION TARRIES, WHILE SUNDAY MORNING APPROACHETH."

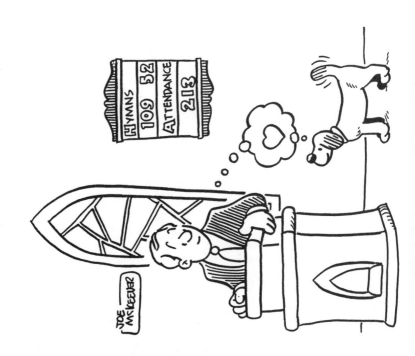